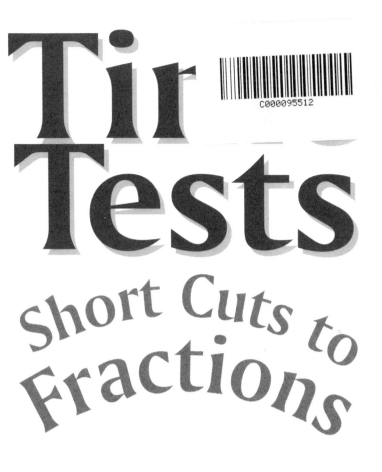

Tir Tests

Tests

Short Cuts to Fractions

by Norman D Lock
cover illustration by Gary Slater

A catalogue record for this book is available from the British Library

Published by Ladybird Books Ltd
27 Wrights Lane London W8 5TZ
A Penguin Company

2 4 6 8 10 9 7 5 3 1

© LADYBIRD BOOKS LTD MM
text © Norman D Lock MCMXCV

Test 1

1	5
2	x 4
3	add 4
4	÷ 3
5	$\frac{1}{2}$ of this
6	times by 4
7	− 1
8	divide by 3
9	multiply by itself
10	minus 6

What is your answer?

Check your answer at the back of the book.

Record your time on the Record Sheet.

Test 2

1	three
2	+ 4
3	times by 2
4	− 5
5	÷ 3
6	x 5
7	plus 1
8	half of this
9	half of this
10	add on 6

What is your answer?

Check your answer at the back of the book.

Record your time on the Record Sheet.

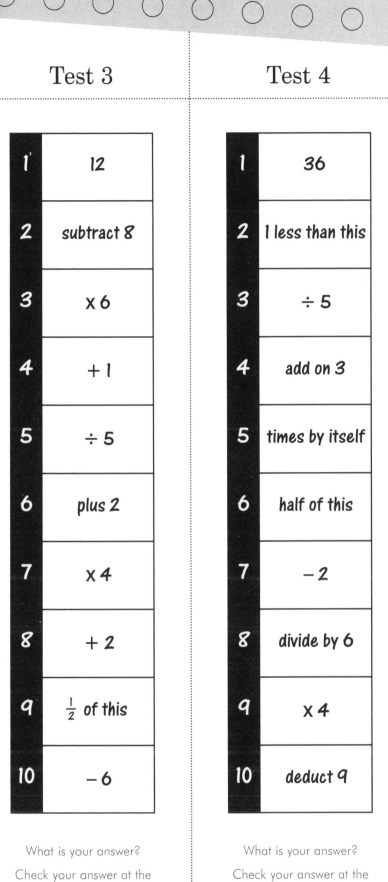

Test 3

1	12
2	subtract 8
3	x 6
4	+ 1
5	÷ 5
6	plus 2
7	x 4
8	+ 2
9	$\frac{1}{2}$ of this
10	− 6

What is your answer?

Check your answer at the back of the book.

Record your time on the Record Sheet.

Test 4

1	36
2	1 less than this
3	÷ 5
4	add on 3
5	times by itself
6	half of this
7	− 2
8	divide by 6
9	x 4
10	deduct 9

What is your answer?

Check your answer at the back of the book.

Record your time on the Record Sheet.

Test 5

1	nine
2	X 3
3	+ 9
4	share into 6 equal parts
5	X 7
6	3 more
7	÷ 9
8	double it
9	X 7
10	half of it

What is your answer?

Check your answer at the back of the book.

Record your time on the Record Sheet.

Test 6

1	17
2	take away 5
3	÷ 4
4	8 lots of this
5	double it
6	+ 1
7	divide by 7
8	X 8
9	plus 4
10	$\frac{1}{2}$ of it

What is your answer?

Check your answer at the back of the book.

Record your time on the Record Sheet.

When you want $\frac{1}{2}$ of something, split it into **2 equal parts**. Divide by 2 like this:

$\frac{1}{2}$ of 8

| 4 | 4 | ← $\frac{1}{2}$ of 8 is 4

When you want $\frac{1}{3}$ of something, split it into **3 equal parts**. Divide by 3 like this

$\frac{1}{3}$ of 15

| 5 | 5 | 5 | ← $\frac{1}{3}$ of 15 is 5

To find $\frac{1}{4}$ of something, **divide by 4**, and so on.

How do you find $\frac{1}{5}$ of something?

Yes, **divide it by 5**.

$\frac{1}{5}$ of 20

| 4 | 4 | 4 | 4 | 4 |

$\frac{1}{5}$ of 20 is 4

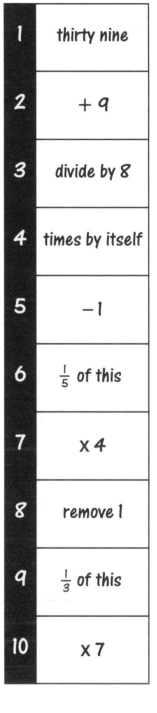

1	thirty nine
2	+ 9
3	divide by 8
4	times by itself
5	− 1
6	$\frac{1}{5}$ of this
7	× 4
8	remove 1
9	$\frac{1}{3}$ of this
10	× 7

What is your answer?

Check your answer at the back of the book.

Record your time on the Record Sheet.

Test 8

1	18
2	$\frac{1}{6}$ of this
3	+ 8
4	double it
5	− 1
6	$\frac{1}{3}$ of this
7	× by itself
8	+ 1
9	$\frac{1}{2}$ of this
10	− 7

What is your answer?

Check your answer at the back of the book.

Record your time on the Record Sheet.

Test 9

1	thirty
2	one fifth of this
3	× 7
4	+ 3
5	÷ 9
6	multiply by itself
7	+ 7
8	a quarter of this
9	plus 6
10	half of it

What is your answer?

Check your answer at the back of the book.

Record your time on the Record Sheet.

Test 10

1	thirteen
2	double it
3	ten more
4	$\frac{1}{4}$ of this
5	times by itself
6	− 9
7	$\frac{1}{8}$ of this
8	+ 5
9	half of this
10	x 4

What is your answer?

Check your answer at the back of the book.

Record your time on the Record Sheet.

Test 11

1	16
2	plus seventeen
3	− 9
4	one sixth of this
5	x by itself
6	double it
7	$\frac{1}{8}$ of this
8	+ 7
9	x 4
10	5 extra

What is your answer?

Check your answer at the back of the book.

Record your time on the Record Sheet.

Test 12

1	60
2	subtract 6
3	$\frac{1}{9}$ of this
4	+ 2
5	multiply by itself
6	− 4
7	one quarter of this
8	$\frac{1}{5}$ of this
9	× 8
10	a half of this

What is your answer?

Check your answer at the back of the book.

Record your time on the Record Sheet.

Test 13

1	four
2	times by seven
3	+ 14
4	$\frac{1}{7}$ of this
5	plus nineteen
6	double it
7	+ 6
8	one eighth of this
9	+ 15
10	$\frac{1}{2}$ of this

What is your answer?

Check your answer at the back of the book.

Record your time on the Record Sheet.

Test 14

1	33
2	add fifteen
3	$\frac{1}{4}$ of this
4	one sixth of this
5	x 9
6	multiply by 2
7	6 more
8	$\frac{1}{7}$ of this
9	times by 9
10	minus 5

What is your answer?

Check your answer at the back of the book.

Record your time on the Record Sheet.

Test 15

1	twenty three
2	deduct 8
3	x 2
4	increase by 9
5	÷ 3
6	double it
7	remove 1
8	÷ 5
9	multiply by 8
10	one quarter of this

What is your answer?

Check your answer at the back of the book.

Record your time on the Record Sheet.

Another way of saying

'Times that number by itself' is **'Square that number.'**

Squares are made by using certain numbers of small squares to build bigger squares, like this:

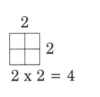

$2 \times 2 = 4$

$3 \times 3 = 9$

2 squared is 4
3 squared is 9
4 squared is 16

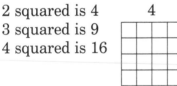

$4 \times 4 = 16$

A quick way of writing **3 squared** is 3^2.

$3^2 = 9$ $4^2 = 16$
$5^2 = 25$ $6^2 = 36$

From now on, when you have to **square** a number you will be shown n^2. The **n** stands for the number that you have reached at that point.

To continue the test, you square that number and move on to the next instruction.

1	*nineteen*
2	*plus 18*
3	-5
4	$\frac{1}{8}$ *of this*
5	n^2
6	$+ 8$
7	*one third of this*
8	*subtract 5*
9	n^2
10	$+ 6$

What is your answer?

Check your answer at the back of the book.

Record your time on the Record Sheet.

Test 17

1	ten
2	n^2
3	one quarter of this
4	$\frac{1}{5}$ of this
5	$+ 3$
6	n^2
7	remove 10
8	$\div 6$
9	increase by 4
10	double it

What is your answer?

Check your answer at the back of the book.

Record your time on the Record Sheet.

Test 18

1	70
2	half of it
3	$+ 5$
4	share out into 5 equal parts
5	add on 4
6	times by 5
7	$\frac{1}{10}$ of it
8	n^2
9	$+ 12$
10	one eighth of it

What is your answer?

Check your answer at the back of the book.

Record your time on the Record Sheet.

Test 19

1	8
2	9 times this
3	− 16
4	one seventh of this
5	× 5
6	one tenth of this
7	add 5
8	n^2
9	+ 19
10	$\frac{1}{5}$ of this

What is your answer?

Check your answer at the back of the book.

Record your time on the Record Sheet.

Test 20

1	fourteen
2	+ 16
3	× 2
4	3 extra
5	one ninth of this
6	− 5
7	n^2
8	n^2
9	increase by 20
10	$\frac{1}{4}$ of this

What is your answer?

Check your answer at the back of the book.

Record your time on the Record Sheet.

As well as squaring numbers, you can find the **square root** of numbers. The **square root** of 16 is 4, because 4 x 4 = 16.

The **square root** of 25 is 5, because 5 x 5 = 25.

Can you think what the square root of 49 is?

Yes, it's 7, because 7 x 7 = 49.

There is a special sign used for **square root**. It looks like this $\sqrt{}$ and fits over the top of a number.

$\sqrt{36} = 6$ $\sqrt{100} = 10$

From now on, when you have to find the **square root** of a number, you will be shown $\sqrt{n}$.

Remember that **n** stands for the number you have reached at that point.

1	55
2	plus 9
3	$\sqrt{n}$
4	x 7
5	16 fewer than this
6	+ 2
7	$\frac{1}{3}$ of this
8	half of this
9	n^2
10	− 30

What is your answer?

Check your answer at the back of the book.

Record your time on the Record Sheet.

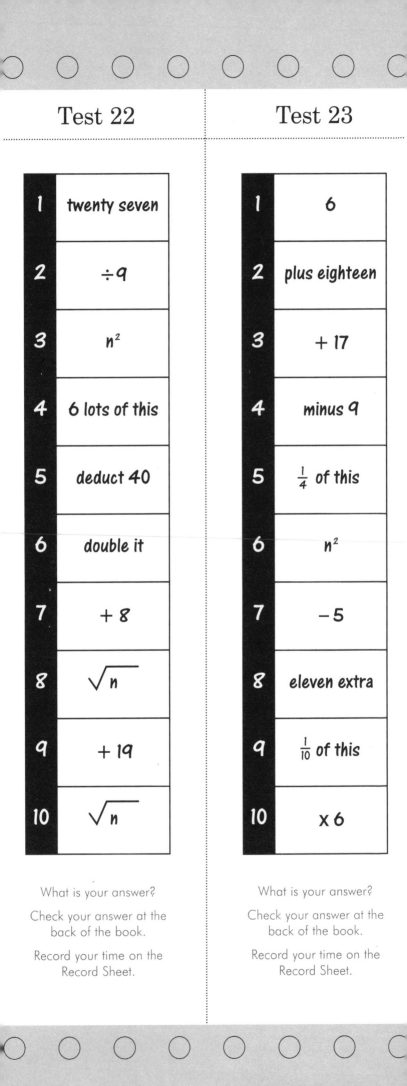

Test 22

1	twenty seven
2	$\div 9$
3	n^2
4	6 lots of this
5	deduct 40
6	double it
7	$+ 8$
8	$\sqrt{n}$
9	$+ 19$
10	$\sqrt{n}$

What is your answer?

Check your answer at the back of the book.

Record your time on the Record Sheet.

Test 23

1	6
2	plus eighteen
3	$+ 17$
4	minus 9
5	$\frac{1}{4}$ of this
6	n^2
7	$- 5$
8	eleven extra
9	$\frac{1}{10}$ of this
10	$\times 6$

What is your answer?

Check your answer at the back of the book.

Record your time on the Record Sheet.

Test 24

1	7
2	times by 3
3	add on one hundred
4	$\sqrt{n}$
5	double it
6	− 4
7	divide by 3
8	n^2
9	plus 6
10	$\frac{1}{7}$ of this

What is your answer?

Check your answer at the back of the book.

Record your time on the Record Sheet.

Test 25

1	thirty one
2	+ 19
3	add on another four
4	$\frac{1}{6}$ of this
5	$\sqrt{n}$
6	x 7
7	plus forty
8	− 12
9	$\sqrt{n}$
10	x 8

What is your answer?

Check your answer at the back of the book.

Record your time on the Record Sheet.

Test 26

1	eleven
2	− 6
3	n^2
4	four times this
5	$\sqrt{n}$
6	one tenth of this
7	× 19
8	add twenty three
9	÷ 7
10	multiply by 3

What is your answer?

Check your answer at the back of the book.

Record your time on the Record Sheet.

Test 27

1	43
2	deduct 30
3	double it
4	ten less than this
5	$\sqrt{n}$
6	× 9
7	double it
8	divide by 8
9	n^2
10	− 15

What is your answer?

Check your answer at the back of the book.

Record your time on the Record Sheet.

To find $\frac{1}{3}$ of something, split it into **3 equal parts**.

$\frac{1}{3}$ of 24

8	8	8

Each part is $\frac{1}{3}$

$\frac{1}{3}$ of 24 is 8

So, $\frac{2}{3}$ will be 2 of these parts.

$\frac{2}{3}$ of 24 is 16

To find $\frac{3}{4}$ of 20, split 20 into **4 equal parts** (quarters).

5	5	5	5

$\frac{1}{4}$ of 20 is 5

$\frac{3}{4}$ of 20 is 15

$\frac{1}{4}$ of 20 is $20 \div 4 = 5$

$\frac{3}{4}$ will be 3 lots of $5 = 15$

Find $\frac{3}{5}$ of 10:

2	2	2	2	2

$\frac{1}{5}$ of 10 is 2

$\frac{3}{5}$ of 10 is 6

1	15
2	$\frac{2}{3}$ of this
3	× 4
4	divide by 8
5	n^2
6	plus eleven
7	$\sqrt{n}$
8	times by 3
9	+ 3
10	one seventh of this

What is your answer?

Check your answer at the back of the book.

Record your time on the Record Sheet.

Test 29

1	26
2	times by 0
3	add 12
4	$\frac{3}{4}$ of this
5	− 2
6	n^2
7	− 14
8	$\frac{2}{7}$ of this
9	n^2
10	half of this

What is your answer?

Check your answer at the back of the book.

Record your time on the Record Sheet.

Test 30

1	eight
2	x 6
3	$\frac{1}{2}$ of this
4	$\frac{2}{3}$ of this
5	$\sqrt{n}$
6	times by 8
7	double it
8	$\sqrt{n}$
9	x 5
10	$\frac{3}{4}$ of this

What is your answer?

Check your answer at the back of the book.

Record your time on the Record Sheet.

Test 31

1	one hundred
2	$- 19$
3	$\sqrt{n}$
4	$\sqrt{n}$
5	$\times 8$
6	$+ 1$
7	double it
8	$\frac{3}{5}$ of this
9	$+ 6$
10	$\sqrt{n}$

What is your answer?

Check your answer at the back of the book.

Record your time on the Record Sheet.

Test 32

1	2
2	times by three
3	multiply by four
4	$\frac{5}{6}$ of this
5	add on eighty
6	$\sqrt{n}$
7	$\times 7$
8	plus two
9	$\div 8$
10	$\sqrt{n}$

What is your answer?

Check your answer at the back of the book.

Record your time on the Record Sheet.

Test 33

1	forty four
2	100 more
3	$\sqrt{n}$
4	x 2
5	$\frac{3}{8}$ of this
6	n^2
7	− 9
8	divide by 9
9	n^2
10	half of it

What is your answer?

Check your answer at the back of the book.

Record your time on the Record Sheet.

Test 34

1	33
2	$\frac{1}{3}$ of this
3	x 4
4	4 more
5	$\frac{5}{8}$ of this
6	$\frac{2}{3}$ of this
7	+ 5
8	$\sqrt{n}$
9	x 7
10	double it

What is your answer?

Check your answer at the back of the book.

Record your time on the Record Sheet.

Test 35

1	one
2	times 79
3	two more
4	$\sqrt{n}$
5	x 4
6	one sixth of this
7	multiply by 5
8	remove 17
9	add ninety
10	take 3

What is your answer?

Check your answer at the back of the book.

Record your time on the Record Sheet.

Test 36

1	87
2	deduct forty
3	+ 2
4	$\sqrt{n}$
5	6 times this
6	subtract 10
7	$\frac{3}{4}$ of this
8	+ seventy
9	minus four
10	$\frac{3}{10}$ of this

What is your answer?

Check your answer at the back of the book.

Record your time on the Record Sheet.

Test 37

1	twenty five
2	$\frac{3}{5}$ of this
3	$\frac{2}{3}$ of this
4	n^2
5	-36
6	$\frac{5}{8}$ of this
7	plus two
8	$\div 7$
9	multiply by nine
10	minus 5

What is your answer?

Check your answer at the back of the book.

Record your time on the Record Sheet.

Test 38

1	24
2	19 extra
3	remove 8
4	$\frac{3}{7}$ of this
5	double it
6	double it
7	$\frac{5}{6}$ of this
8	-18
9	divide equally into four parts
10	x 9

What is your answer?

Check your answer at the back of the book.

Record your time on the Record Sheet.

As well as multiplying by whole numbers, it is also possible to **multiply by whole numbers and fractions.**

Look at these examples:

$1\frac{1}{2}$ x 6 means:

1 x 6 + $\frac{1}{2}$ x 6, or

1 lot of $6 = 6$, + $\frac{1}{2}$ of $6 = 3$

$1\frac{1}{2}$ x $6 = 9$

$1\frac{1}{4}$ x 8 means:

1 x 8 + $\frac{1}{4}$ x 8, or

1 lot of $8 = 8$, + $\frac{1}{4}$ of $8 = 2$

$1\frac{1}{4}$ x $8 = 10$

$2\frac{1}{3}$ x 12 means:

2 x 12 + $\frac{1}{3}$ x 12, or

2 lots of $12 = 24$, + $\frac{1}{3}$ of 12 $= 4$

$2\frac{1}{3}$ x $12 = 28$

You can also think of it in another way:

6 x $1\frac{1}{2}$ means:

6 x 1 + 6 x $\frac{1}{2}$, or

6 lots of $1 = 6$, + 6 lots of $\frac{1}{2}$ $= 3$

6 x $1\frac{1}{2} = 9$

1	30
2	$\frac{3}{5}$ of this
3	+ 17
4	÷ 7
5	double it
6	$2\frac{1}{2}$ times this
7	 $\sqrt{n}$
8	multiply by 8
9	$\frac{4}{5}$ of this
10	half of it

What is your answer?

Check your answer at the back of the book.

Record your time on the Record Sheet.

Test 40

1	twelve
2	$1\frac{1}{3}$ times this
3	$\sqrt{n}$
4	× 9
5	double it
6	$\frac{5}{8}$ of this
7	subtract 3
8	÷ 6
9	n^2
10	eleven extra

What is your answer?

Check your answer at the back of the book.

Record your time on the Record Sheet.

Test 41

1	50
2	take off 19
3	10 fewer than this
4	$\frac{5}{7}$ of this
5	double it
6	$2\frac{1}{3}$ times this
7	+ 11
8	$\sqrt{n}$
9	times by 4
10	$\sqrt{n}$

What is your answer?

Check your answer at the back of the book.

Record your time on the Record Sheet.

Test 42

1	sixteen
2	$1\frac{1}{4}$ times this
3	$\frac{3}{5}$ of this
4	$2\frac{1}{2}$ times this
5	x 5
6	take away 6
7	$\sqrt{n}$
8	9 extra
9	double it
10	cut up into 6 equal parts

What is your answer?

Check your answer at the back of the book.

Record your time on the Record Sheet.

Test 43

1	8
2	$5\frac{3}{4}$ times this
3	add eighteen
4	$\sqrt{n}$
5	multiply by 7
6	plus two hundred
7	− 6
8	$\frac{1}{2}$ of it
9	subtract 25
10	$\sqrt{n}$

What is your answer?

Check your answer at the back of the book.

Record your time on the Record Sheet.

Test 44

1	twenty
2	× 8
3	add on 9
4	$\sqrt{n}$
5	− 2
6	6 times this
7	take off 10
8	$\frac{3}{8}$ of this
9	times by three
10	divide by 7

What is your answer?

Check your answer at the back of the book.

Record your time on the Record Sheet.

Test 45

1	19
2	increase by 16
3	multiply by 3
4	− 51
5	÷ 9
6	n^2
7	$\frac{5}{9}$ of this
8	$2\frac{3}{4}$ times this
9	$\frac{2}{5}$ of this
10	nine more

What is your answer?

Check your answer at the back of the book.

Record your time on the Record Sheet.

Test 46

1	seventeen
2	double it
3	double it
4	+ 2
5	$\frac{4}{10}$ of this
6	remove 5
7	3 lots of this
8	+ 3
9	$\frac{2}{9}$ of this
10	$2\frac{1}{4}$ times this

What is your answer?

Check your answer at the back of the book.

Record your time on the Record Sheet.

Test 47

1	60
2	$\frac{2}{3}$ of this
3	x 5
4	decrease by 4
5	$\sqrt{n}$
6	$1\frac{1}{2}$ times this
7	4 times this
8	− 3
9	$\sqrt{n}$
10	multiply by 7

What is your answer?

Check your answer at the back of the book.

Record your time on the Record Sheet.

Test 48

1	88
2	$\frac{7}{8}$ of this
3	− 5
4	$\frac{8}{9}$ of this
5	$\sqrt{n}$
6	$6\frac{1}{4}$ times this
7	double it
8	− 1
9	$\frac{3}{11}$ of this
10	× 3

What is your answer?

Check your answer at the back of the book.

Record your time on the Record Sheet.

Test 49

1	seventy
2	$\frac{1}{2}$ of it
3	remove 1
4	divide by 2
5	3 lots of this
6	deduct one
7	$\frac{9}{10}$ of this
8	decrease by 3
9	$1\frac{1}{2}$ times this
10	÷ 9

What is your answer?

Check your answer at the back of the book.

Record your time on the Record Sheet.

Test 50

1	five hundred
2.	$\frac{1}{2}$ of it
3	− 25
4	$\sqrt{n}$
5	four lots of this
6	$\frac{7}{10}$ of this
7	take away 13
8	+ 70
9	$\frac{4}{9}$ of this
10	$\frac{3}{4}$ of this

What is your answer?

Check your answer at the back of the book.

Record your time on the Record Sheet.

Test 51

1	29
2	double it
3	remove 6
4	one quarter of this
5	x 3
6	add eleven
7	$3\frac{1}{2}$ times this
8	− 94
9	$\frac{7}{9}$ of this
10	$\frac{4}{7}$ of this

What is your answer?

Check your answer at the back of the book.

Record your time on the Record Sheet.

Record Sheet

Date	Test No.	Time	Score

Record Sheet

Date	Test No.	Time	Score

Record Sheet

Date	Test No.	Time	Score